Usborne Workbooks

Spelling

This book belongs to

....

There are answers on page 27, and notes
for grown-ups at the back of the book.

Here are some of the animals you'll meet in this book.
Help them practise their letters by tracing over the dotted lines.
Start at the big dot and follow the arrows.

Say each letter sound out loud as you write it.

Coco the raccoon

Olly the owl

Bun the rabbit

Squilly the squirrel

Hug the bear

Spike the hedgehog

Grown-ups – When you practise spelling with your child,
say the letter sounds and not the letter names (say 'sss' not 'ess').

Usborne Workbooks
Spelling

Illustrated by Maddie Frost

Written by Jane Bingham
Designed by Meg Dobbie

You can use a pen or pencil to write in this book.

Stripe the badger

Help US spell.

Foxy the fox

Mo the mouse

Moley the mole

At the end of the book there are blank pages for more spelling practice.

Edited by Kristie Pickersgill
Series Editor: Felicity Brooks

Beginnings and endings

Help Moley find the right letter to begin these words. Say what you see in the picture on each blue card and listen to its starting sound. Then write the letter that makes that sound. (The first one has been done.)

Choose from these starting letters:

w s d b h c

d o _

_ u _

_ e _

_ e _

_ a _

_ u _

Now say each word again and write the letter that makes its ending sound.

Choose from these ending letters:

t g n d b p

Missing middles

Each of these words is missing a middle letter.
Help Squilly pick one letter from the vowel tree
to complete each word.

Remember! The five vowels are a, e, i, o and u. The other letters in the alphabet are called consonants.

c _ t

l _ g

b _ g

p _ n

b _ b

e   i

a

o   u

Vowel Tree

Can you make two new words by writing a vowel in each gap below?

bug > b _ g   pen > p _ n

Now use different vowels to make two more words.

bug > b _ g   pen > p _ n

Say the new words out loud as you write.

k or c?

Sometimes, the letter **c** makes a sound like a **k.** Can you help Bun and her family choose a **k** or a **c** to start their words?

Words usually start with k when their second letter is i or e.

Words usually start with c when their second letter is a, o or u.

Try to _eep up!

Look at that _olourful _ite!

I love _arrots!

What a _ute _aterpillar!

Write two words of your own that start with a **k** sound.

k _____   c _____

Can you think of two more words with a **k** starting sound?

k _____   c _____

k or ck?

You can use **k** or **ck** to spell the **k** sound at the end of a word.
Look at the animals' boards, then help Spike to complete his signs.

If the word ends in e, you use a k before the e.

cake

You use a k if the word has two vowels in a row.

book

For most other words, you use ck.

duck

Should Spike use **ke**, **k** or **ck**? Add the right endings to his signs.

Loo_ out!

Thi__ weeds

Deep la__

Don't get stu__!

Twit twoo!

Remember! The five vowels are a, e, i, o and u.

Two letters, one sound

Help the animals finish their kites by adding a sound made from two letters. Look at the pictures on the kites and write two letters to complete each word. Then draw a string to match each kite to the right owner.

__ip   ri__   __ick   mo__

ch   sh   th   ng

Now complete these kites by adding two letters to the end of each word.

pea__   fi__   too__   stri__

Twit twoo!

Notice how the letter pairs work together to make a single sound.

Double letters

Four of the words in this box end in a double letter. Underline the double letters and say the sounds they make.

sing   buzz   dash   yell

miss   hold   puff   kick

Can you complete these words by adding double letters?

Choose from these double letters:

ss zz ll ff

Foxy set o _ _ fast.

But he fe _ _ over.

Foxy lay on the gra _ _ .

He saw Bun whi _ _ past him!

The double letters ff, ll, ss and zz make a single sound. They often come at the end of a word.

Sound blends

Some consonants blend together to make a sound. Can you fill in the missing sound blends in this story? Foxy has done the first one.

When you have used a sound blend, draw a line through it.

sn   st   gl   sp   gr   thr   scr   ~~fr~~   dr

One day, two **fr**iends __otted

a __ake __iding ___ough

the __ass. Coco __opped her

bag and ___eamed, but Hug

__opped to say hello.

Hello!

Eeeeek!

Twit twoo!

Remember! A consonant is any letter of the alphabet except a, e, i, o or u.

Stripe is drawing a line between all the words that end in the same sound. Can you help her? There should be three words in each group.

board

bunk

Notice how the two ending letters blend together to make a sound.

think

stamp

card

lump

word

tank

jump

Now complete the words on the green leaves. Then draw a line to link each word to another word on this page with the same ending sound.

la _ _

bi _ _

i _ _

Tricky sounds

Sometimes, you use **wh** to spell the **w** sound and **ph** to spell the **f** sound. Can you help Mo add **wh** or **ph** to complete her words?

__ __ ale   __ __ eel

__ __ oto   __ __ one

Most question words start with the letters **wh**.
Can you fill in the missing question words?

Why

What

_____ do you live?

___ is the sky blue?

Where

When

____ is your name?

____ will it get dark?

Foxy's magic

Foxy is adding the letter **e** to his words. Can you help him? Read the words out loud and listen to how they change when you add **e**.

The letter **e** is magic!

The **e** is silent but it makes the words sound different.

hop > hop**e**

tub > tub _

tap > tap _

bit > bit _

not > not _

Hey presto!

Now add a letter **e** to make three new words and say them out loud. Listen to the way the sound of the word changes.

cub _   man _   kit _

Twit twoo!

When you add the letter e to the end of a word, it turns the first vowel into a long sound (a sound that takes longer to say).

Same sound, different spellings

Some sounds can be spelled in more than one way. Look at the different spellings below. Then help the mice spell their words.

train   coin   tray   toy

You use ai and oi in the middle of a word.

You use ay and oy at the end of a word.

Can you choose the right spellings for these words?

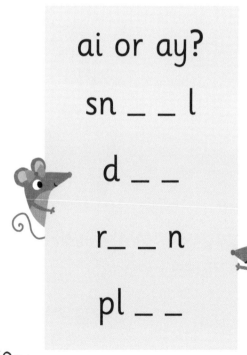

ai or ay?

sn _ _ l

d _ _

r _ _ n

pl _ _

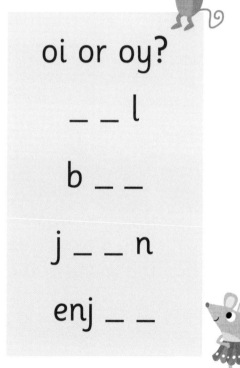

oi or oy?

_ _ l

b _ _

j _ _ n

enj _ _

Twit twoo!

The English language has many sounds that can be spelled in different ways. It takes lots of practice to get the spellings right!

Stripe's story

There are many ways to spell the sound **or**. Mo is pointing to some of the spellings here.

| or | al | ore | au | aw | oor | oar |

Can you pick the right spellings in Stripe's story? Draw a line through the words you think are wrong.

One m**aw**ning/m**or**ning, Stripe went for a w**al**k/w**aw**k. She wanted to expl**ore**/expl**oor**, but she soon got lost.

Spike felt sad bec**or**se/bec**au**se she couldn't find her house. When she s**aw**/s**au**r her d**or**/d**oor**, she gave a r**oar**/r**or** of joy!

> You could practise writing any words you find tricky on the blank pages at the back of the book.

Find the rhyme

Words that rhyme, such as bed and red, have the same ending sound.
Can you help Hug and Squilly find pairs of rhyming words?
Draw a line between the words that rhyme.

Say each word out loud and listen to its sound.

snail

toad

leaf

fly

train

thief

tie

plane

whale

code

Now write a rhyming word with three letters on each empty sign.

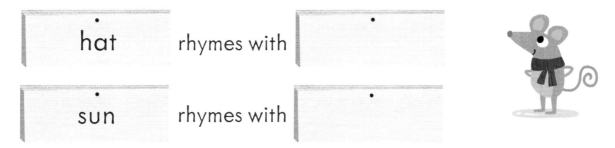

hat   rhymes with

sun   rhymes with

Can you think of any more words that rhyme with 'hat' or 'sun'?
Write them on the blank pages at the back of the book.

Spike's syllables

Spike is saying words out loud to see how many syllables (or beats) they have. Count the syllables in the words on the cards. Then draw a line to the birdhouse with the right number.

cobweb

drag-on-fly
has 3 syllables.

dragonfly

pear

berry

caterpillar

1

2

3

4

Can you count the syllables in these animal words?
The first one has been done for you.

rabbit **2**   badger   butterfly

Twit twoo!

bear   woodpecker   hedgehog

If you break up a word into syllables, it will be easier to spell.

Making new words

Some words are made by adding two words together. Can you help the animals do these word sums to make new words?

Can you do the next one?

sun + flower = sunflower

star + fish =

tooth + brush =

Draw a line between two words that make sense when you put them together. Then write the new word you've made.

straw	cake	___cake
snow	berry	_____berry
cup	flake	____flake

Twit twoo!

Words made by joining two words together are called compound words.

Singular and plural

Bun is sorting clothes. Can you help her?
Draw a line from each label to the right basket.

Singular means one of something. Plural means more than one of something.

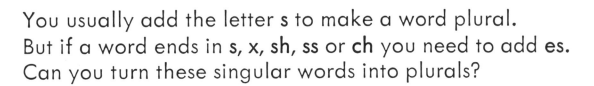

You usually add the letter **s** to make a word plural.
But if a word ends in **s, x, sh, ss** or **ch** you need to add **es**.
Can you turn these singular words into plurals?

box ____    peach ____

shell ____    feather ____

dish ____    bus ____

Yum!

Remember! Look out for words that end in **s, x, sh, ss** or **ch**.

Changing words

When you add **ing** or **ed** to a word, you change its meaning.

These words all belong to the same word family.

dress   dress**ing**   dress**ed**

Can you complete these sentences by adding **ing** or **ed**?

Coco likes paint___.

She paint__ the fence.

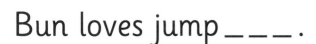

Bun loves jump___.

She jump__ over Moley.

Bun land__ in a puddle.

Stripe couldn't stop laugh___.

Hee hee hee!

Now add **er** and **est** to change the meaning of this word.

small   small _ _   small _ _ _

The animals are taking part in competitions. Can you fill in the gaps, using words ending in **er** or **est**?

Wow!

high   high _ _   h _ _ _ _ _ _

Yay!

fast   fast _ _   f _ _ _ _ _ _

loud   loud _ _   l _ _ _ _ _ _

Moley's diary

Moley's diary has one mistake in each line. Draw a ring around the word you think is wrong. Then write the correct spelling on the line below. You can check your words on page 27.

On Monday, I saw my (frend.)

friend

On Tuesday, we went on a buss.

_ _ _

On Wednesday, we played in the parc.

_ _ _ _

On Thursday, I went to skool.

_ _ _ _ _

On Friday, we played at my hows.

_ _ _ _

Now try writing your own sentence for Saturday.

 On Saturday, we

Squilly's list

Squilly is writing a list of things he has seen in the wood. Can you help him spell his words?

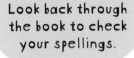

Look back through the book to check your spellings.

In the wood I saw...

A s _ _ _ _

A f _ _ on a l _ _ _

A s _ _ _ _ in the g _ _ _ _ _

Two f _ _ _ _ on a l _ _

Now write some more things Squilly has spotted. Look through the book to give you ideas. You can draw some pictures too, if you like.

Spelling quiz

Find out how much you can remember about spelling by doing this quiz.
The answers are on page 26.

1. Can you spot the five vowels in this sentence?
   Underline each vowel.

   ## Bun likes carrots.

2. Stripe needs to add two letters to each of his words. Draw a line to join
   the start of each word to the right ending. Then write out the words.

   a) pu   ng   _ _ _ _

   b) clo   ch   _ _ _ _ _

   c) thi   th   _ _ _ _ _

   d) bea   sh   _ _ _ _ _

3. Moley is counting the syllables in her words. Help her by writing
   the number of syllables beside each word.

   a) zebra   ☐   d) hippopotamus   ☐

   b) rhinoceros   ☐   e) elephant   ☐

   c) horse   ☐

4. Can you help Foxy find the rhyming pairs? Draw a line between the words that rhyme.

sheep	sail
mug	socks
head	slug
fox	bed
pale	leap

5. Does Spike need to add 's' or 'es' to these words to make them plural? Tick the correct box.

	s	es
a) fox	☐	☐
b) clock	☐	☐
c) beach	☐	☐
d) class	☐	☐
e) rabbit	☐	☐

6. Can you add the right endings to the words in this story?

est ed er ing

The animals held a jump _ _ _ competition.

Foxy jump_ _ high _ _ than Moley.

Bun's jump was the high _ _ _ .

7. Look at the picture clues. Then help Squilly spell the words to complete the crossword.

ACROSS

3.

5.

6.

DOWN

1.

2.

4.

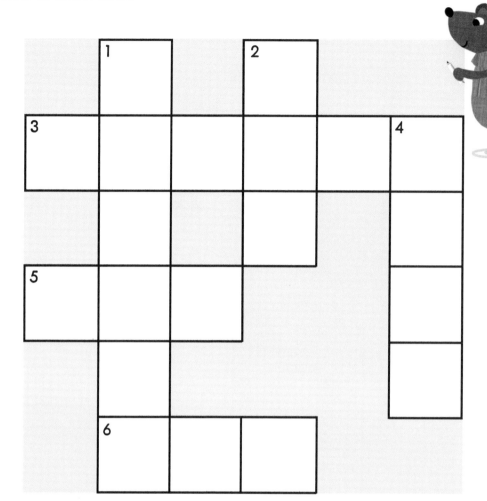

Answers

Pages 4-5

dog, cup, bed, web, hat, sun
cat, bug, log, pen, bib
bug > bag, beg, big or bog   pen > pan, pin or pun

Pages 6-7

keep, colourful, kite, carrots, cute, caterpillar
Look out! Thick weeds Deep lake Don't get stuck!

Pages 8-9

ship, ring, chick, moth
peach, fish, tooth, string
buzz, yell, miss, puff
off, fell, grass, whizz

Pages 10-11

friends, spotted, snake, gliding, through, grass, dropped, screamed, stopped
bunk, think, tank, ink   board, card, word, bird   stamp, lump, jump, lamp

Page 12

whale, wheel, photo, phone
where, why, what, when

Pages 14-15

snail, day, rain, play   oil, boy, join, enjoy
morning, walk, explore, because, saw, door, roar

Pages 16-17

snail/whale toad/code leaf/thief fly/tie train/plane
hat rhymes with bat, cat, fat, mat, pat, rat, sat, tat, vat
sun rhymes with bun, dun, fun, gun, nun, pun, run
There are also some longer words that rhyme with hat and sun.
cobweb 2; dragonfly 3; pear 1; berry 2; caterpillar 4
rabbit 2; badger 2; butterfly 3; bear 1, woodpecker 3; hedgehog 2

Don't worry if you made some mistakes. You can rub or cross out your answers and try again.

Pages 18-19

sunflower, starfish, toothbrush   cupcake, strawberry, snowflake
singular – coat, hat; plural – gloves, socks
boxes peaches shells feathers dishes buses

Pages 20-21

painting, painted, jumping, jumped, landed, laughing
small, smaller, smallest; high, higher, highest;
fast, faster, fastest; loud, louder, loudest

Pages 22-23

friend, bus, park, school, house
snail, fly, leaf, snake, grass, foxes, log

You can use these pages to practise your spelling.

How many words can you think of that start with a 'k' sound?

Write them on this page. You could draw a picture for each one.

Can you spell
the names of
the things on
this page?

Now draw
one more of each thing.
Can you turn your singular
words into plurals?

Which words do you find hard to spell? Try writing them on this page.

You can use a dictionary to check your spellings.

Notes for grown-ups

Beginnings and endings/Missing middles (pages 4-5)

These activities provide practice in recognizing sounds (phonemes) and linking them to letters (graphemes). Children work with CVC (consonant, vowel, consonant) words and are introduced to vowels and consonants.

k or c?/k or ck? (pages 6-7)

On these pages, children are introduced to alternative spellings for the k sound and given guidance and practice in using these spellings.

Two letters, one sound/Double letters (pages 8-9)

Here, children are introduced to consonant digraphs (two consonants together) that produce a single sound. Page 8 covers digraphs made from two different consonants. Page 9 covers double consonants at the end of words.

Sound blends (pages 10-11)

These pages introduce the use of consonant clusters (digraphs and trigraphs) to create a blended sound. Children are given practice in recognizing these sound blends at the start and end of words.

Tricky sounds/Foxy's magic (pages 12-13)

On page 12, children are introduced to the consonant blends ph and wh, and are given practice in using them. Page 13 shows what happens when the letter e is added to the end of a word to create a split digraph (two sounds interrupted by a different sound). When an e is added, two vowel sounds are split by a consonant. The first vowel sound becomes long and the second is silent.

Same sound, different spellings/Stripe's story (pages 14-15)

Page 14 gives guidance and practice in spellings using ay/ai and oy/oi. Page 15 provides practice for alternative ways of spelling the 'or' sound.

Find the rhyme/Spike's syllables (pages 16-17)

These pages encourage reading aloud and careful listening. The rhyming activity helps children recognize that different spellings can create the same sound. The syllables activity shows children how to break up words into segments as an aid to spelling.

Making new words/Singular and plural (pages 18-19)

Page 18 introduces the concept of making compound words by joining two words together. Page 19 introduces the rule for creating regular plurals and for creating plurals for words ending in s, x, sh, ss or ch.

Changing words (pages 20-21)

These activities provide practice in adding the suffixes -ing, -ed, -er and -est to a root word. Only root words that remain unchanged are introduced here.

Moley's diary/Squilly's list (pages 22-23)

Page 22 provides spelling practice for some common exception words. Page 23 gives children an opportunity to revise some of the spellings covered in the book.